GW00646353

Electronic Keyboard
Grade 1

Pieces & Technical Work
for Trinity College London exams

2015-2018

Published by:
Trinity College London
www.trinitycollege.com

Registered in England
Company no. 02683033
Charity no. 1014792

Copyright © 2014 Trinity College London
Second impression, October 2015

Printed in England by Caligraving Ltd.

Whirling Dervishes

Andrew Smith

Voice: Accordion
Style: Dance

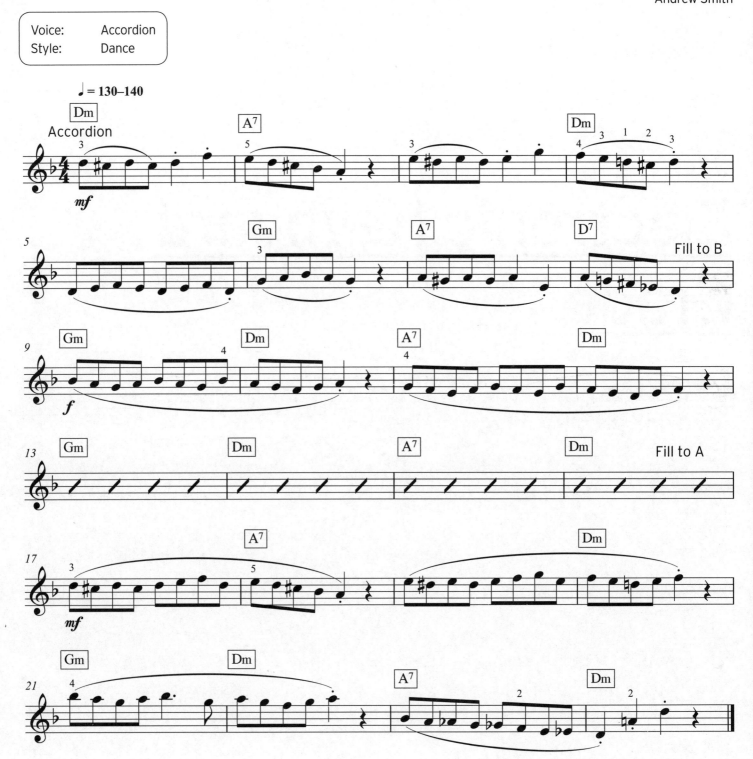

PLEASE SET UP FOR THE NEXT PIECE

Scarborough Fair

Traditional
arr. Andrew Smith

Voices: Bassoon, Strings
Style: Waltz

PLEASE SET UP FOR THE NEXT PIECE

It's Gonna be Good

Nancy Litten

Voice:	Lead Guitar
Style:	Hard Rock

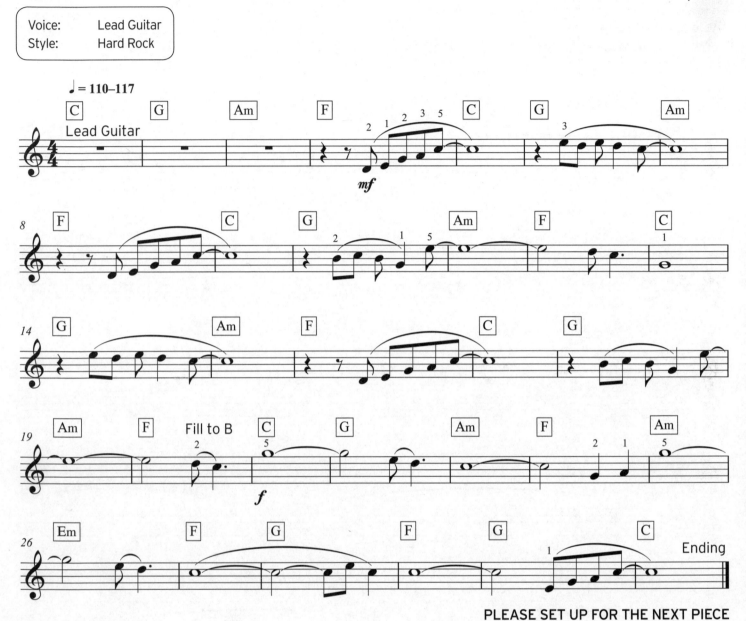

PLEASE SET UP FOR THE NEXT PIECE

La donna è mobile

Giuseppe Verdi
arr. Victoria Proudler

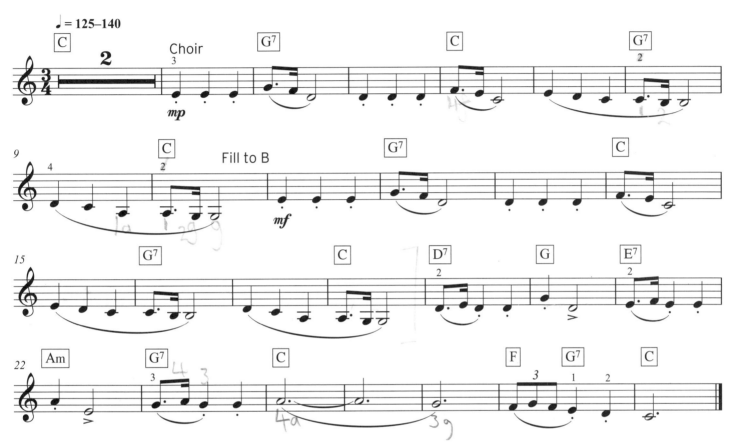

PLEASE SET UP FOR THE NEXT PIECE

Home on the Range

Daniel E Kelley

arr. Rory Marsden

Voices: Fiddle *or* Violin, Harmonica
Style: Country Waltz (Swing feel)

Own Interpretation*

Swing Low, Sweet Chariot

Traditional
arr. Joanna Clarke

Voice: ~~Flute 65~~ Trumpet -57
Style: 68 SlowRk -20

PLEASE SET UP FOR THE NEXT PIECE

* Candidates should refer to the current syllabus requirements for Own Interpretation pieces.

The Ash Grove

Traditional
arr. Nancy Litten

Voices: Oboe, Strings
Style: English Waltz *or* Serenade

PLEASE SET UP FOR THE NEXT PIECE

The Great Escape

Elmer Bernstein

arr. Joanna Clarke

Voices: Brass, Whistle
Style: March

PLEASE SET UP FOR THE NEXT PIECE

Romance de Amor

Traditional
arr. Andrew Smith

Voices: Classical *or* Acoustic Guitar (sounding octave lower),
Piccolo (sounding octave higher)
Style: ⁶⁄₈ Ballad

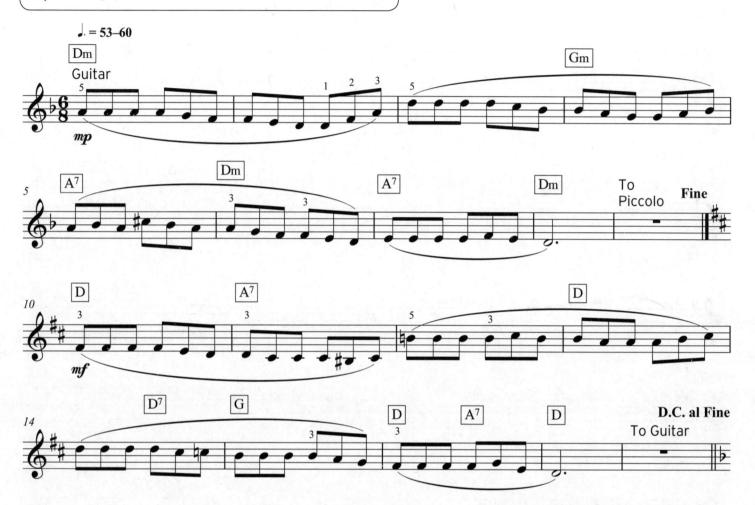

PLEASE SET UP FOR THE NEXT PIECE

La Cucaracha

Traditional
arr. Jeremy Ward

Voice: Steel Drums
Style: Salsa *or* Rhumba

Fill to B

PLEASE SET UP FOR THE NEXT PIECE

Technical Work

Technical work – candidates to prepare in full *either* section i) *or* section ii)					

either **i) Scales & chord knowledge** (from memory) – the examiner will select from the following:					
F and G major				hands separately	
D and E minor (candidate's choice of either harmonic *or* melodic *or* natural minor)		one octave			piano voice with auto-accompaniment off
Pentatonic scales starting on G and F (5 notes)					
Chromatic scale in contrary motion starting on D	min. ♩ = 70		*legato* and *mf*	hands together	
C major contrary motion scale		two octaves			
Triad of F and G major, D and E minor (root position and first inversion)				L.H. only	
Chord of F⁷ and G⁷ (root position and first inversion)					

or **ii) Exercises** (music may be used):	
Candidates to prepare **all** three exercises. The candidate will choose one exercise to play first; the examiner will then select one of the remaining two exercises to be performed.	
Swaying	keyboard functions exercise
Spinning Wheel	scalic exercise
Parade	pianistic exercise

Please refer to the current syllabus for details on all elements of the exam

i) Scales & chord knowledge

F major scale (one octave)

Right hand

Left hand

G major scale (one octave)

Right hand

Left hand

D minor scale: harmonic (one octave)

Right hand

Left hand

D minor scale: melodic (one octave)

Right hand

Left hand

D minor scale: natural (one octave)

Right hand

Left hand

E minor scale: harmonic (one octave)

Right hand

Left hand

13

E minor scale: melodic (one octave)

Right hand

Left hand

E minor scale: natural (one octave)

Right hand

Left hand

Chromatic scale in contrary motion starting on D (one octave)

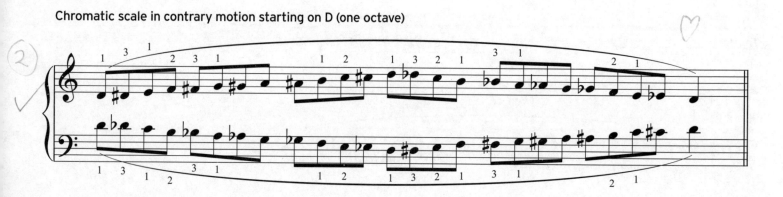

Pentatonic scale starting on G (five notes)

Right hand

Left hand

Pentatonic scale starting on F (five notes)

Right hand

Left hand

C major contrary motion scale (two octaves)

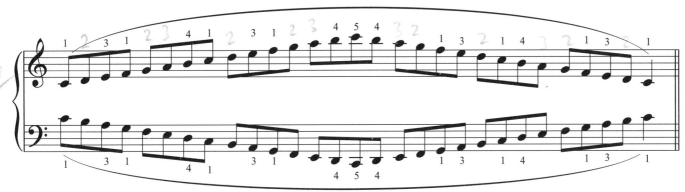

F major

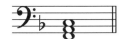 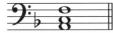

G major

 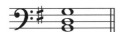

D minor

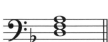 

E minor

F^7

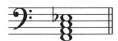 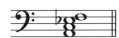

G^7

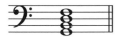 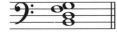

ii) Exercises

1. Swaying – keyboard functions exercise

Voice:	Flute
Style:	Waltz

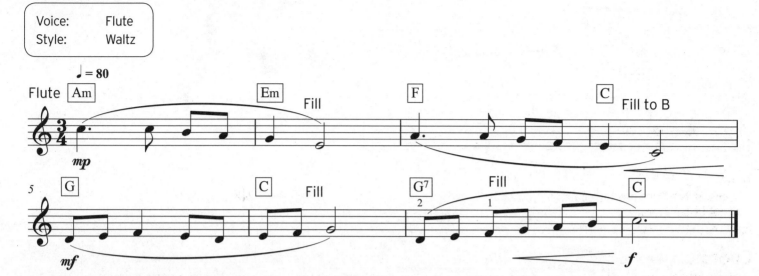

2. Spinning Wheel – scalic exercise

Voice:	Harp
Style:	8 Beat

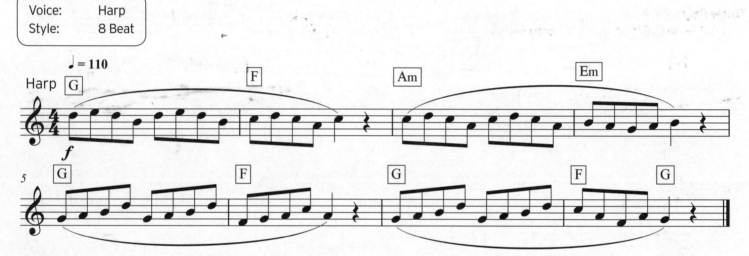

3. Parade – pianistic exercise

Voice:	Piano
Style:	None